The Best
Liverpool F.C
Trivia Book Ever

300+ Interesting Trivia Questions and Random,
Shocking, Fun Facts Every Red Devils Fan Needs to Know

House of Ballers

YOUR FREE BONUS!

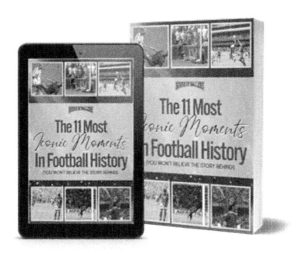

- What did Materazzi say to earn a headbutt from Zidane on the biggest stage of them all?
- Who got shot for scoring an own goal at the World Cup?
- What did Maradona reveal on his autobiography about the 'Hand of God'?

Find out by scanning the QR Code below with your smartphone:

Contents

INTRODUCTION

The fans of Liverpool F.C are some of the proudest fans in the world of football, and rightly so. Liverpool F.C, or The Reds, as they are fondly called, is a super club located in Northwestern England that has contributed immensely to the rich history of European football. Where excellence, trophies and success are mentioned in a discussion about English football, Liverpool are never far away.

Liverpool F.C's history has always been colourful, right from its origins. Founded in 1892 after a dispute between Everton and the owner of Anfield (Everton's stadium at the time), Liverpool has since grown to become arguably the greatest sporting institution in Britain. The aftermath of that dispute resulted in the formation of the Reds and they have gone from leaps to bounds.

As one half of the fierce Merseyside derby, Liverpool F.C has provided some of the most exciting moments in European Football history. For most of the second half of the 20th century, they were the team to beat in England and they arguably had the best-ever period of dominance in English football in the 1970s and 1980s.

In the first half of the 20th century, Liverpool had recorded 5 First Division titles, but by the 1953/54 season, the Reds were relegated to the Second Division. That disappointment was very short-lived, though. By the end of that decade, Bill Shankly was appointed as the manager and his first acts were to release 24 players in preparation for his extensive rebuild of the Liverpool first team and convert an old Boot Room into a strategy room where he could discuss tactics extensively with his assistants. Promotion was secured in 1962; the league title followed in 1964; the first FA Cup trophy was secured in 1965, and then another league title and an appearance in the European Cup Winner's Cup final were delivered in 1966.

Shankly's success inspired a generation of dominance from Liverpool. Upon his retirement, Bob Paisley stepped into the role with even more success to show for it – 20 trophies in 9 seasons. Joe Fagan and Kenny Daglish were the next to fill the shoes to great success but in the beginning of the 1990s, perennial rivals, Manchester United and their own legendary boss, Alex Ferguson, upstaged the Reds as the dominant force. That led the Reds to a league-winning drought of 30 years. Even in this period, though, the Reds continued to deliver maximum entertainment and trophies including multiple League Cup and F.A cup victories, and of course, *the miracle of Istanbul.*

Threatened bankruptcy in 2010 led to a change of ownership and in 2015, Jurgen Klopp sauntered in as head coach with his German brand of gegenpressing and attacking football. It took some time to rebuild the team but aided by the mega sale of Coutinho, his efforts finally paid off with a UCL trophy in 2019, a record Premier League title and a Club World Cup trophy in 2020. The Reds belong at the top, as it should be.

For more than a century, Anfield has been a slaughterhouse for opponents from all over the world. Hearing The Kop roar on European nights has sent shivers down the spines of many big European giants before kickoff and there are very few rivals who relish a trip to face the Reds in that cauldron of noise, belief and passion.

In the 130 years of their existence, The Reds have seen it all. The crazy comeback in Istanbul; the buzzing matches against Everton and Manchester United; legends like Steven Gerrad, Sir Kenny Daglish; loyalty and devotion personified in flamboyant personalities like Rafa Benitez; the absolute wizardry from the likes of Owen, Suarez and Ian Rush, and even the sad emotions that trailed the Heysel and Hillsborough disasters.

FORTY-FIVE loyal captains after formation, Liverpool boasts of nineteen League titles, seven FA Cup triumphs, Fifteen Community Shields, Nine League Cups, Six European Cups, Three UEFA Cups, Four UEFA Super Cups and one FIFA Club World Cup. No other English club can boast of a bigger haul!

Today, Liverpool F.C has evolved from just a football club – it is a mega business entity with annual revenues greater than $600 million, an institution of momentous size, and above all, a family of passion-driven, success-loving football fans from all over the world. With 200 Official Supporters' clubs in over 50 countries, Liverpool FC's family is as large as they come.

But how much do you really know about the history, origins and structure of Liverpool F.C? Do you really know the greatest values that have been sewn into the fabric of the football club? Can you comfortably state the facts that tell the story of Liverpool F.C's glorious past?

It doesn't matter what your answers to the questions above were. This trivia book has been written to boost your knowledge of Liverpool F.C. And it WILL!

In the next twelve chapters filled with trivia questions and amazing facts, you will be taken through a RED journey like no other. We will talk through

You will be feted with statistics that will BLOW your mind and stories that will WOW you. This book will take you to the hallowed grounds of Anfield and allow you to relive glorious European nights, long past. Do you want to relive Luis Suarez's brilliance? Do you want to be taken through Steven Gerrad's excellent strike against A.C Milan? Do you know the number of goals Ian Rush scored for Liverpool F.C in his glittering career?

Are you ready for this treat of a lifetime? Do you want to be able to share facts and stats with other members of the Red family?

Get right in!

With the Reds, *You'll Never Walk Alone!!!*

ORIGIN

"If Shankly was the Anfield foreman, Paisley was the brickie, ready to build an empire with his own hands"

- Tommy Smith

20 Trivia Questions

1. What is the symbol on the crest of Liverpool FC?

    A. Liver Bird

    B. Seagull

    C. Liver Goose

    D. Bee

2. In what year was Liverpool FC founded?

    A. 1890

    B. 1892

    C. 1894

    D. 1896

3. What is the anthem of Liverpool FC?

    A. "We are on your side"

    B. "Glory Glory Liverpool"

    C. "Red is the colour"

    D. "You'll never walk alone"

4. In what year did Liverpool win their first ever league title?

   A. 1900

   B. 1901

   C. 1902

   D. 1903

5. Who is the most decorated Liverpool player?

   A. Phil Neal

   B. Roger Hunt

   C. Ian Rush

   D. Ian Callaghan

6. Who was the first manager of Liverpool FC?

   A. Bob Paisley

   B. Graeme Souness

   C. Bill Shankly

   D. John McKenna

7. In which season was Liverpool FC first elected into the football league?

   A. 1893/94

   B. 1892/93

   C. 1894/95

   D. 1891/92

8. Who were the opponents for Liverpool's first ever match?

    A. Luton Town

    B. Rotherham Town

    C. Accrington Stanley

    D. Huddersfield Town

9. Who founded Liverpool FC?

    A. John Houlding

    B. John McKenna

    C. John Smith

    D. John Harris

10. In what year did Liverpool win their second league title?

    A. 1904

    B. 1906

    C. 1908

    D. 1910

11. Who was the club's first ever shirt sponsor?

    A. Candy

    B. Carlsberg

    C. Crown Paints

    D. Hitachi

12. Who was Liverpool's first ever league opponent?

    A.   Middlesbrough

    B.   Huddersfield Town

    C.   Bolton Wanderers

    D.   Nottingham Forest

13. Which of these key moments in the history of the club came first?

    A.   Liverpool wins its third European Cup

    B.   Ian Rush signs for the club

    C.   Liverpool earns a shirt sponsorship

    D.   Bruce Grobbelaar becomes Liverpool's number one goalie

14. In which season did Liverpool adopt an all-red kit for their home league matches?

    A.   1965/66

    B.   1966/67

    C.   1967/68

    D.   1968/69

15. What was the scoreline in Liverpool's first ever match in 1892?

    A.   5:1

    B.   5:2

    C.   7:1

    D.   7:2

16. Who was Liverpool's first ever opponent in the FA Cup final?

    A. Burnley

    B. Gillingham

    C. Arsenal

    D. Chelsea

17. Which club did Liverpool face in their second FA Cup final in 1950?

    A. Chelsea

    B. Everton

    C. Queens Park Rangers

    D. Arsenal

18. Who was the first Liverpool player to lift the FA Cup trophy?

    A. Ian St John

    B. Ian Callaghan

    C. Tommy Smith

    D. Ron Yeats

19. Apart from geographical location, which other(s) factor led to the club being named Liverpool FC?

    A. The club's directors desire to get more fans

    B. The FA rejected other names

    C. The club board approved the name

    D. The club was founded by a Mayor in Liverpool

20. Who was Liverpool FC's first European opponent?

A. KR Reykjavik

B. Anderlecht

C. Koln

D. Milan

20 Trivia Answers

1. A – Liver Bird

2. B – 1892

3. D – "You'll never walk alone"

4. B – 1901

5. A – Phil Neal

6. D – John McKenna

7. A – 1893/94

8. B – Rotherham Town

9. A – John Houlding

10. B – 1906

11. D – Hitachi

12. A – Middlesbrough

13. C – Liverpool earns a shirt sponsorship

14. A – 1965/66

15. C – 7:1

16. A – Burnley

17. D – Arsenal

18. D - Ron Yeats

19. B – The FA rejected other names

20. A – KR Reykjavik

10 Fun Facts

1. Liverpool Football Club is named after the city of Liverpool, one of the most famous locations in the Northwest of England. Liverpool is also home to another Premier League side, Everton FC. Both clubs have one of the most colorful and engaging derby rivalry in English League history

2. Liverpool initially intended to be called Everton Athletic but the English Football Association would not register them as such because there already existed a team with a similar name.

3. Liverpool Football Club was founded on March 15 1892 after a disagreement between the directors on the board of Everton FC and chairman John Houlding, to whom the club's ground, Anfield, belonged to. A dispute due to rent prompted Everton's move away from Anfield.

4. Left with an empty ground following Everton's move to Goodison Park, John Houlding decided to form Liverpool FC. The club joined the Lancashire league and went on to clinch the championship in their first season.

5. Following the resignation of Accrington and Bootie, Liverpool FC were accepted into the Football League in the 1893-94 season. They went on to win the Second Division in their first season in the Football League.

6. Liverpool's first sustained period of success came following the appointment of Tom Watson as manager in 1896. He led the club to its first Division One title in 1901. Another league title followed in 1906 and he also led the club to a first FA Cup final in 1914, falling to defeat at the hands of Burnley.

7. Liverpool have not always appeared in their now traditional all-red colours. The club spotted a kit made up of a light blue and white quartered shirt with dark blue shorts and socks for the first 4 years. The club adopted red shirts, white shorts and red socks in 1896.

8. Liverpool's nickname is "The Reds" which comes from the club's colours of red but it only stuck when the club switched to donning red shorts and socks in 1965 at the request of legendary manager, Bill Shankly.

9. Liverpool FC initially adopted the city of Liverpool's coat of arms as its logo. The crest has undergone several medications over the years, often retaining a Liver bird and the name of the football club.

10. The Shankly Gates and the lyrics of the club's anthem "You'll Never Walk Alone" were introduced onto the commemorative centenary crest for the 1992-93 season. Eternal flames were also introduced a year later to honour the memory of victims of the Hillsborough disaster.

STADIUM

"There's no noise like the Anfield noise"

-Ian St John

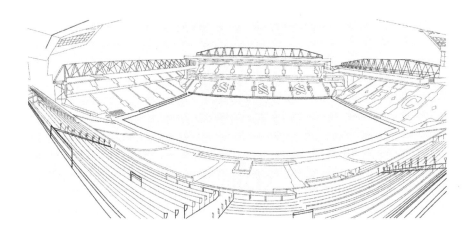

20 Trivia Questions

1. What are the words written on the stairs leading to the pitch in Liverpool's home ground?

   A. You'll Never Walk Alone

   B. We are the Reds

   C. This is Anfield

   D. The Home of Football

2. Which room was used by the club's coaching staff to discuss tactics between the 1960s and 1990s?

   A. The Ball Room

   B. The Red's Room

   C. The Smart Room

   D. The Boot Room

3. In 2018, what was the Centenary Stand in Liverpool's home ground renamed to?

   A. The Graeme Souness Stand

   B. The Kenny Daglish Stand

   C. The Steven Gerrard Stand

   D. The Jamie Carragher Stand

4. What are the terraces at Liverpool's home ground known as?

    A. The Kip

    B. The Kop

    C. The Kap

    D. The Kup

5. Which of these stadiums is the club's home ground?

    A. Signal Iduna Park

    B. Reds Arena

    C. Hawthorns

    D. Anfield

6. Which of these is a stand in the club's home ground?

    A. Spion Kop

    B. Marrow Stand

    C. Reds Stand

    D. Shankly Stand

7. What was the Centenary stand formerly called?

    A. East Stand

    B. Kemlyn Road Stand

    C. The Paddock

    D. Glawdys Street Stand

    E.

8. Which of these are spelt out on the lower tier of the Centenary stand?

    A. L.F.C

    B. ANFIELD

    C. THE KOP

    D. THE REDS

9. In what year was the electronic scoreboard installed at the club's home ground?

    A. 2002

    B. 2003

    C. 2004

    D. 2005

10. What is the estimated seating capacity of the club's stadium?

    A. 50,394

    B. 55,394

    C. 53,394

    D. 57,394

11. Which other club once used Liverpool's home ground?

    A. Everton

    B. Aston Villa

    C. West Bromwich Albion

    D. Norwich City

    E.

12. What is the dimension of the pitch at Liverpool's home ground?

    A. 113.5yd X 77.4yd

    B. 112.5yd X 76.4yd

    C. 111.5yd X 75.4yd

    D. 110.5yd X 74.4yd

13. In what year was Liverpool's stadium originally opened?

    A. 1881

    B. 1882

    C. 1883

    D. 1884

14. What is the record attendance at Liverpool's home ground?

    A. 55,905

    B. 58,905

    C. 61,905

    D. 63,905

15. In what year was Liverpool's stadium converted to an all-seater stadium?

    A. 1994

    B. 1995

    C. 1996

    D. 1997

16. Which one of these is a gate in Liverpool's home ground?

    A. Ian Rush Gate

    B. Bob Paisley Gate

    C. Elisha Scott Gate

    D. Robbie Fowler Gate

17. In what year was the Bill Shankly's statue outside the club's stadium unveiled?

    A. 1995

    B. 1996

    C. 1997

    D. 1998

18. Which of these stands is the Bob Paisley statue located closest to?

    A. The Main Stand

    B. The Sir Kenny Daglish Stand

    C. The Spion Kop Stand

    D. The Anfield Road End Stand

19. Which of these individuals was the original owner of the club's home ground?

    A. Billy Connor

    B. Mark Gallagher

    C. John Houlding

    D. John Orell

20. Which of these stands is the oldest stand at the club's home ground?

    A. The Anfield Road End

    B. The Sir Kenny Daglish Stand

    C. The Main Stand

    D. The Spion Kop Stand

20 Trivia Answers

1.   C – This is Anfield

2.   D – The Boot Room

3.   B – The Kenny Daglish Stand

4.   B – The Kop

5.   D – Anfield

6.   A – Spion Kop

7.   B – Kemlyn Road Stand

8.   A - L.F.C

9.   B – 2003

10.   C – 53,394

11.   A – Everton

12.   D – 110.5yd X 74.4yd

13.   D – 1884

14.   C – 61,905

15.   A – 1994

16.   B – Bob Paisley Gate

17.   C – 1997

18.   A – The Main Stand

19.   C – John Houlding

20.   C – The Main Stand

10 Fun Facts

1. Anfield is the home ground of Liverpool FC. It used to be home to local rivals Everton before a rent dispute led to their departure for Goodison Park, less than a mile from Anfield.

2. Anfield has a capacity of 54,074 and opened in 1884. The first game it hosted was between Everton and Earlestown in 1884 which was won 5-0 by Everton.

3. Liverpool's first game at Anfield was a friendly exhibition against Rotherham Town on September 1, 1892 which the home team won 7-1.

4. Anfield has four main all-seater stands; the Anfield Road End, the Sir Kenneth Dalglish Stand, the Kop End, and the Main Stand.

5. The Main Stand was first built in 1895 by renowned architect Archibald Leitch. It had a capacity of 3,000. After that came the Anfield Road Stand in 1903 followed by a stand called the Spion Kop along the Walton Breck Road in 1906. Another stand was built around the same time along the Kemlyn Road.

6. The first major redevelopment of the ground took place in 1928 when the Kop was redesigned and extended to hold a standing capacity of 30,000 spectators. The old Kemlyn Road stand was replaced in 1963 and ten years later, the old Main stand was partially demolished and extended backwards with new roof and lights.

7. The highest attendance record at Anfield is 61,905 during the Reds FA Cup fifth round tie against Wolverhampton Wanderers on February 2 1952.

8. The Shankly Gates were constructed in 1982 as a tribute to legendary former manager Bill Shankly. The lyrics "You'll Never Walk Alone" from the club's anthem feature prominently at the top. The Hillsborough memorial is located alongside the Shankly Gates.

9. The Kemlyn Road Stand was renamed as the Centenary Stand to commemorate the club's 100 years of existence in 1992. It was renamed again in 2017 to honour former player and manager Sir Kenneth Dalglish.

10. Liverpool FC have had Anfield as their home ground for the entirety of their existence. Chelsea are the only other current top flight club who have never changed their grounds.

MANAGERS

"If Shankly was the Anfield foreman, Paisley was the brickie, ready to build an empire with his own hands"

- Tommy Smith

20 Trivia Questions

1. Which of these former Liverpool managers has a brown belt in judo?

    A. Kenny Dalglish

    B. Brendan Rodgers

    C. Rafael Benitez

    D. Gerard Houllier

2. Where did former Liverpool manager, Bill Shankly, spend most of his playing career?

    A. Liverpool FC

    B. West Ham United

    C. Preston North End

    D. Birmingham

3. Which one of these former Liverpool managers was not Scottish?

    A. Graeme Souness

    B. Kenny Daglish

    C. Bill Shankly

    D. Brendan Rodgers

    E.

4. Which manager led Liverpool to win the 2005 Champions League?

    A. Roy Hodgson

    B. Rafael Benitez

    C. Kenny Dalglish

    D. Brendan Rodgers

5. Who was the first player signed by Jurgen Klopp?

    A. Sadio Mane

    B. Joel Matip

    C. Georginio Wijnaldum

    D. Marko Grujic

6. Who is the club's longest-serving manager (by length of stay)?

    A. Tom Watson

    B. George Patterson

    C. Bob Paisley

    D. Don Welsh

7. Which of these managers managed the most matches for Liverpool?

    A. Tom Watson

    B. Phil Taylor

    C. David Ashworth

    D. Bill Shankly

    E.

8. Which of these managers replaced Bill Shankly as Liverpool manager?

   A.   Tom Watson

   B.   Bob Paisley

   C.   Joe Fagan

   D.   Reuben Bennett

9. In what year was Bill Shankly appointed as manager?

   A.   1955

   B.   1957

   C.   1959

   D.   1961

10. Which of the following managers was not in charge of Liverpool FC during the 90s?

   A.   Gerard Houllier

   B.   Graeme Souness

   C.   Roy Evans

   D.   Bill Shankly

11. Which German club did the current Liverpool FC manager, Jurgen Klopp, spend most of his playing career with?

   A.   Freiburg

   B.   Mainz 05

   C.   Leipzig

   D.   Cologne

12. Who is the most decorated Liverpool manager?

    A. Bob Paisley

    B. Rafael Benitez

    C. Bill Shankly

    D. Jurgen Klopp

13. Which of these clubs did Bill Shankly leave to manage Liverpool?

    A. Grimsby Town

    B. Huddersfield Town

    C. Carlisle United

    D. Preston North End

14. In what year did Bill Shankly die?

    A. 1978

    B. 1979

    C. 1980

    D. 1981

15. Who was Liverpool's manager in the 2010/2011 season?

    A. Brendan Rodgers

    B. Rafael Benitez

    C. Roy Hodgson

    D. Kenny Daglish

16. Which of these managers made the club a force to be reckoned with in the 1960s to 1980s?

    A. Bill Shankly

    B. Joe Fagan

    C. Bob Paisley

D. Kenny Daglish

17. Who was Liverpool's manager when Ian Rush scored 47 goals in a single season?

A. Graeme Souness

B. Bob Paisley

C. Kenny Daglish

D. Joe Fagan

18. Who was Bob Paisley's first signing for Liverpool?

A. Terry McDermott

B. Ray Kennedy

C. Phil Neal

D. Peter McDonnell

19. How many Liverpool games did Roy Hodgson oversee as a manager?

A. 30

B. 31

C. 32

D. 33

20. Which of these managers signed Michael Robinson for the club?

A. Joe Fagan

B. Bob Paisley

C. Bill Shankly

D. Kenny Daglish

20 Trivia Answers

1. C – Rafael Benitez

2. C – Preston North End

3. D – Brendan Rodgers

4. B – Rafael Benitez

5. D – Marko Grujic

6. A – Tom Watson

7. D – Bill Shankly

8. B – Bob Paisley

9. C – 1959

10. D – Bill Shankly

11. B – Mainz 05

12. A – Bob Paisley

13. B – Huddersfield Town

14. D – 1981

15. C – Roy Hodgson

16. A – Bill Shankly

17. D – Joe Fagan

18. D – Peter McDonnell

19. B – 31

20. A – Joe Fagan

10 Fun Facts

1. Tom Watson is the longest serving manager in Liverpool history. His appointment in 1896 heralded the first successful spell in the club's history. He won the First Division twice and the FA Cup once during a 19-year stay at the club.

2. Bill Shankly took charge of the Reds for 783 games from 1959 to 1974, the most of any Liverpool manager. He won 3 First Division titles, 2 FA Cups, 1 UEFA Cup and 4 Charity Shields as manager. He is widely regarded as the greatest manager in the history of Liverpool football club and local factory workers threatened industrial action when he announced his departure from the club.

3. Shankly's assistant, Bob Paisley, took over from him in 1974 and continue the Reds dominance by winning 6 league titles, 3 European Cups, 3 League Cups, 5 Charity Shields, 1 UEFA Cup and 1 UEFA Super Cup. Paisley remains the only manager to have won up to 3 European Cups at a single club and is without doubt the most decorated Reds manager of all-time.

4. Paisley kept with tradition by handing over the reins to his assistant Joe Fagan upon his departure. Fagan went on to win the league in his first season as manager, helping the club match the record for successive top flight title wins. He also led the club to League Cup and European Cup success in the same season.

5. Sir Kenneth Dalglish was initially named player-manager before taking the job fulltime upon ending his playing career. He scored the title-winning goal at Stamford Bridge and also won the FA Cup in his first season in charge. He won six major trophies across two spells as Liverpool manager. He however was not fortunate to lead the Reds in Europe as English clubs had been banned for five years in the aftermath of the Heysel stadium disaster of 1985.

6. Don Welsh was the first manager to be sacked by Liverpool FC. He led the club

to its last relegation from the top flight in the 1955-54 season. The Reds had only suffered relegation on two other occasions before then.

7. Gerard Houlier led Liverpool to only their second treble success in 2001, masterminding triumphs in the UEFA Cup, League Cup and FA Cup. He was plagued by heart problems the following season, which kept him out of the dugout for about five months. However, the club still managed to achieve a second-place finish in the league.

8. Having led Spanish side Valencia to two titles in 3 seasons between 2002-04, Rafael Benitez took over the reins at Liverpool following the departure of Gerard Houlier. He instantly went on to become only the third person to lead the Reds to European Cup/UEFA Champions League glory, edging out AC Milan 3-2 on penalties in arguably the most memorable final in the history of the competition.

9. Jurgen Klopp is the first, and so far, only German to win the Premier League title after he led the Reds to a first top flight crown in 30 years in 2020. The Reds wrapped up the title with seven games of the league campaign left, a record. Liverpool finished the season on 99 points, just one point behind the Premier league record of 100 set by Manchester City in 2018.

10. Jurgen Klopp is only the fourth Liverpool boss to lead the club to European Cup/UEFA Champions league success, helping the club to a sixth such crown in 2019. He also led the club to a first Club World Cup title later that year.

GOALIES

"Sometimes I feel I'm hardly wanted in this Liverpool team. If I get two or three saves to make, I've had a busy day"

- Ray Clemence

20 Trivia Questions

1. Which of these players was not a Liverpool goalie?

   A.   David Raven

   B.   Scott Carson

   C.   Jerzy Dudek

   D.   Pepe Reina

2. Which of these goalies was the fastest to keep 100 clean sheets for the club?

   A.   David James

   B.   Elisha Scott

   C.   Bruce Grobbelaar

   D.   Pepe Reina

3. Which season did former Liverpool goalie, Simon Mignolet make his Liverpool debut?

   A.   2011/12

   B.   2012/13

   C.   2013/14

   D.   2014/15

4. Against which of these clubs was Pepe Reina shown a red card?

    A. Chelsea & Newcastle

    B. Arsenal & Norwich City

    C. Burnley & Blackburn Rovers

    D. Watford & Burnley

5. Which of these goalies scored a famous late goal against West Brom?

    A. Pepe Reina

    B. Alisson Becker

    C. Loris Karius

    D. Jerzy Dudek

6. Against which club did Kelleher make his Liverpool debut?

    A. Ajax

    B. Newcastle United

    C. Lille

    D. MK Dons

7. Which one of these Liverpool goalies won a Championship medal as an outfield player?

    A. Matt McQueen

    B. Alisson Becker

    C. David James

    D. Jerzy Dudek

    E.

8. Who saved two penalties for Liverpool in the 2005 European Cup final?

    A. Pepe Reina

    B. Jerzy Dudek

    C. David James

    D. Ray Clemence

9. How many First Division titles did Ray Clemence win with Liverpool?

    A. 3

    B. 4

    C. 5

    D. 6

10. Which national team did Pepe Reina represent?

    A. Portugal

    B. Romania

    C. Switzerland

    D. Spain

11. Which goalie was between the sticks when Liverpool won their fourth (4th) European Cup?

    A. Ray Clemence

    B. Bruce Grobbelaar

    C. Pepe Reina

    D. Tommy Lawrence

12. Which of these goalkeepers managed only one (1) appearance in a Liverpool shirt?

    A. John Jones

    B. Adam Bogdan

    C. Diego Cavalieri

    D. Harry McNaughton

13. How many Premier League clean sheet(s) did Jerzy Dudek keep during the 2004/05 season?

    A. 7

    B. 5

    C. 3

    D. 1

14. Which national team did Simon Mignolet play for?

    A. Spain

    B. Sweden

    C. Bulgaria

    D. Belgium

15. How many clean sheets did Ray Clemence manage for Liverpool in all competitions?

    A. 300

    B. 323

    C. 353

    D. 360

16. How many league goal(s) did Matt McQueen score for Liverpool?

    A. 1

    B. 2

    C. 3

    D. 4

17. From which German club was former Liverpool goalie, Loris Karius, signed from?

    A. Stuttgart

    B. Schalke 04

    C. Augsburg

    D. Mainz 05

18. Which of these goalies was affectionally known as "The Flying Pig"?

    A. Tommy Lawrence

    B. Sam Hardy

    C. Cyril Sidlow

    D. Bill Perkins

19. Which club did Arthur Riley make his 300th appearance for Liverpool against?

    A. Stoke City

    B. Blackburn Rovers

    C. Portsmouth

    D. Middlesbrough

20. How many Premier League assist(s) did David James record during his Liverpool career?

    A. 1

    B. 2

    C. 3

    D. 4

20 Trivia Answers

1. A – David Raven

2. D – Pepe Reina

3. C – 2013/14

4. A – Chelsea & Newcastle

5. B – Alisson Becker

6. D – MK Dons

7. A – Matt McQueen

8. B – Jerzy Dudek

9. C – 5

10. D – Spain

11. B – Bruce Grobbelaar

12. D – Harry McNaughton

13. B – 5

14. D – Belgium

15. B – 323

16. B – 2

17. D – Mainz 05

18. A – Tommy Lawrence

19. D – Middlesbrough

20. B – 2

10 Fun Facts

1. The first goalkeeper to score a goal for Liverpool in the Premier League, Alisson Becker, was the most expensive goalkeeper in the world for a few days before Chelsea broke the record with the signature of Kepa Arrizabalaga. He helped Liverpool claim a sixth Champions League title while winning the Premier League Golden Glove. In his second season, he kept another 15 clean sheets in 29 appearances to help the Reds clinch a maiden Premier League title.

2. Ray Clemence is not only Liverpool's most decorated goalkeeper but also one of the best players in the Reds' history. He kept a club record 323 clean sheets in 665 appearances and missed only a handful of games in his 11-year stay on Merseyside. He won 5 First Division titles, 3 European Cups, 2 UEFA Cups, 1 UEFA Super Cup, 1 FA Cup and 1 League Cup

3. Few Liverpool fans of this millennium would believe Premier League veteran Brad Friedel ever featured for the Reds. He did. The American made 25 Premier League appearances for Liverpool before he was allowed to leave in 2000 as he could not hold down a starting spot. He would go on to become one of the best goalkeepers in Premier League history, making 450 appearances across spells with Blackburn Rovers, Aston Villa and Tottenham Hotspur.

4. Adrian replaced injured first choice Alisson Becker in Liverpool's first Premier League game of the 2019-20 season. He went on to reach near cult hero status mostly due to his heroics in the Reds UEFA Super Cup shootout victory against Chelsea. However, a few error-strewn performances have seen him fall behind Caoimhin Kelleher in the pecking order

5. Bruce Grobbelaar is Liverpool's second most decorated goalkeeper and arguably one of the best African goalkeepers of all time. The Zimbabwean won 6 league titles, 3 FA Cups and a European Cup with the Reds.

6. Like Brad Friedel, David James was another Premier League veteran whose better displays came after he had left the Reds. He was so bad he earned the nickname 'Calamity James" during his stay at Anfield. He went on to keep 169 clean sheets in 672 appearances after leaving Liverpool and was part of Portsmouth's 2008 FA Cup winning team.

7. In arguably the most memorable night in recent Liverpool folklore, Polish goalkeeper Jerzy Dudek make a number of key saves during normal time and saved Andriy Shevchenko's decisive penalty to help Liverpool overcome AC Milan 3-2 and claim a fifth European Cup.

8. Spaniard Pepe Reina kept 134 clean sheets in 285 Premier League appearances for Liverpool. He won a League Cup and FA Cup and was the first Liverpool keeper to win the Premier League Golden Glove. He was also the fastest Liverpool goalkeeper to reach 100 clean sheets, doing so in just 198 games.

9. Current Manchester City goalkeeper, Scott Carson, was once on the books of Liverpool. He made four league appearances for the Reds but never really looked like usurping first choice stopper, Pepe Reina.

10. At one time the most expensive goalkeeper in British football, Sander Westerveld claimed a remarkable five trophies in two years at Liverpool. The feat seems all the more impressive as the Dutchman like a few before him was prone to blunders as evidenced in Liverpool's 5-4 UEFA Cup final win over Deportivo Alaves.

DEFENDERS

"The Anfield atmosphere is difficult to explain, you just have to experience it. Every player should try it at least once in his career"

- Alvaro Arbeloa

20 Trivia Questions

1. Which club did former Liverpool defender; Alan Hansen sign from?

    A. Celtic

    B. Partick Thistle

    C. Rangers

    D. Kilmarnock

2. Who was the defender the club paid a club record fee of £2.5 million for in 1993?

    A. Steve Nicol

    B. Mark Wright

    C. Rob Jones

    D. Neil Ruddock

3. What was the shirt number worn by former Liverpool defender, Jamie Carragher?

    A. 20

    B. 23

    C. 25

    D. 28

4. Which defender did Liverpool sign for a world-transfer record fee in 2018?

    A. Virgil Van Dijk

    B. Andy Robertson

    C. Trent Alexander Arnold

    D. Joel Matip

5. Which club did Trent Alexander-Arnold score his first goal for Liverpool against?

    A. Bayer Leverkusen

    B. Hamburg

    C. Hoffenheim

    D. Hertha Berlin

6. Which of these Liverpool defenders has the most Premier League appearances for the club?

    A. Mark Wright

    B. Stephane Henchoz

    C. Daniel Agger

    D. Dejan Lovren

7. Which of these defenders scored twice in Liverpool's 5:1 win over Arsenal in February 2014?

    A. Daniel Agger

    B. Martin Skrtel

    C. Mamadou Sakho

    D. Kolo Toure

    E.

8. Who did Nat Phillips score his first Liverpool goal against?

    A. Newcastle United

    B. Aston Villa

    C. Burnley

    D. Southampton

9. Which of these Liverpool defenders scored in their 2004/05 Champions League campaign?

    A. Stephane Henchoz

    B. Jamie Carragher

    C. Sami Hyypia

    D. Djimi Traore

10. Which of these Liverpool defenders started their football career at Preston North End?

    A. Mark Lawrenson

    B. Emlyn Hughes

    C. Ron Yeats

    D. Alan Hansen

11. Where was former Liverpool defender, Ragnar Klavan, transferred to?

    A. Sassuolo

    B. Cagliari

    C. Genoa

    D. Sampdoria

12. Which of these defenders scored against Chelsea in the semi-final of the 2007/08 Champions League?

    A. Gabriel Paletta

    B. Daniel Agger

    C. Sami Hyypia

    D. Jamie Carragher

13. Which of these clubs has former Liverpool defender Sami Hyypia NOT managed?

    A. FC Zurich

    B. Bayer Leverkusen

    C. Willem II

    D. Brighton and Hove Albion

14. Who did Joel Matip score his first Liverpool goal against?

    A. Crystal Palace

    B. Southampton

    C. Arsenal

    D. Wolves

15. How many Premier League assists did Andy Robertson end the 2019/20 season with?

    A. 10

    B. 11

    C. 12

    D. 13

16. Which of these defenders scored a goal in the 2012 League Cup final?

    A. Martin Skrtel

    B. Jamie Carragher

    C. Daniel Agger

    D. Glen Johnson

17. Which of these defenders was nicknamed 'Jocky' by fans?

    A. Jamie Carragher

    B. Alan Hansen

    C. Sami Hyypia

    D. Ron Yeats

18. What is the nationality of former Liverpool defender, John Arne Riise?

    A. Irish

    B. Slovakian

    C. Norwegian

    D. Belgian

19. How many titles/trophies did Phil Neal win in total with Liverpool?

    A. 20

    B. 21

    C. 22

    D. 23

20. Who did Virgil Van Dijk open his Liverpool scoring account against?

    A. Brighton and Hove Albion

    B. Newcastle United

    C. Wolverhampton Wanderers

    D. Everton FC

20 Trivia Answers

1.   B – Partick Thistle

2.   D – Neil Ruddock

3.   B – 23

4.   A – Virgil Van Dijk

5.   C – Hoffenheim

6.   C – Daniel Agger

7.   B – Martin Skrtel

8.   C – Burnley

9.   C – Sami Hyypia

10.   A – Mark Lawrenson

11.   B – Cagliari

12.   B – Daniel Agger

13.   C – Willem II

14.   A – Crystal Palace

15.   C – 12

16.   A – Martin Skrtel

17.   B – Alan Hansen

18.   C – Norway

19.   D – 23

20.   C – Wolverhampton Wanderers

10 Fun Facts

1. Portuguese full-back Abel Xavier is the only player who has featured on both sides of the Merseyside divide in the same season. In 2001-02, he played for Everton as they lost 3-1 at home to Liverpool and also played for Liverpool in the 1-1 draw at Anfield layer in the season.

2. English centre back Jamie Carragher has the most appearances for Liverpool in the Premier League era turning out 508 times for the Reds and scoring 3 goals. His total of 737 appearances is bettered only by Ian Callahan's record of 857. He helped the club win the UEFA Champions League, the UEFA Cup, and a host of other domestic honours with the exception of the Premier League.

3. Jaime Carragher scored 8 eight own goals during his Liverpool career, four more than he scored for the Reds. Three of his goals for the club came in the Premier League, and the fourth came in a UEFA Champions League third qualifying round game.

4. Former Slovakian national team captain Martin Skrtel scored seven Premier League own goals during his time at Anfield, level with Reds legend Jaime Carragher, and bettered only by Richard Dunne's record haul of 10.

5. Dutch centre back, Virgil van Dijk, is the second defender to be named Player of the Year in the Premier League era. He claimed the award in 2019 as Liverpool had a near-perfect league campaign losing just once in 38 games and keeping 21 clean sheets.

6. Arguably one of the finest players in Liverpool history, Scotsman Alan Hansen joined the Reds in 1977 from Patrick Thistle and in his first full season helped the club win the first of 3 European Cups during his stay at Anfield.

7. Legendary Liverpool manager Bill Shankly made a bold claim that Ron Yeats would lead Liverpool back to the top flight upon signing the defender in 1961.

Shankly was right as Liverpool won the Second Division and promotion to the top flight less than a year later. Scotsman Yeats helped win Liverpool's first FA Cup in 1965, either side of First Division title successes in 1964 and 1966.

8. Nicknamed 'The Anfield Iron," Tommy Smith enjoyed a stellar 16-year stay at his hometown club, from being a versatile member of Shankly's team to his transformation into a solid and reliable defender who helped Liverpool to their first European Cup in 1977. He won 4 league titles and 2 FA Cups and memorably ended his Anfield career by heading home a corner during the Reds 1977 European Cup final victory against Borussia Monchengladbach.

9. Republic of Ireland centre back, Mark Lawrenson, made 356 appearances for Liverpool following his club record move from Brighton in 1981. He won 5 league titles in 7 years and his formidable partnership with Alan Hansen helped the club to a fourth European Cup in 1984.

10. Early on in his career, Phil Taylor was converted from a forward to a centre back following his 5,000 pounds move to Liverpool from Bristol Rovers in March 1936. He made 345 appearances for the Reds and helped the club win the first league title after World War II. He later managed Liverpool for 3 years from 1956 before handing over the reins to Bill Shankly in 1959.

MIDFIELDERS

"When they start singing 'You'll Never Walk Alone' my eyes start to water. There have been times when I've actually been crying while I've been playing"

- Kevin Keegan

20 Trivia Questions

1. Which of these players wore the famous No. 8 shirt at Liverpool before Steven Gerrard?

    A. Robbie Fowler

    B. Steve McManaman

    C. Emile Heskey

    D. Michael Owen

2. Where was Graeme Souness signed from?

    A. Norwich City

    B. Stoke City

    C. Preston North End

    D. Middlesbrough F.C

3. Which Liverpool midfielder holds the record for the most penalties scored?

    A. Steven Gerrard

    B. Jan Molby

    C. Michael Owen

    D. Roger Hunt

4. Which of these midfielders was nicknamed 'the crazy horse' in the 1970s?

    A. Emlyn Hughes

    B. Ian Callaghan

    C. Jimmy Case

    D. Ray Kennedy

5. Which club did Jordan Henderson spend time on loan at, in 2009?

    A. Coventry City

    B. Derby County

    C. Newcastle

    D. Everton

6. Which country does Naby Keita represent?

    A. Cameroon

    B. Ivory Coast

    C. Senegal

    D. Guinea

7. In what year did James Milner make his Premier League debut?

    A. 2000

    B. 2001

    C. 2002

    D. 2003

8. In which season did Thiago Alcantara make his Liverpool debut?

    A. 2018/19

    B. 2019/20

    C. 2020/21

    D. 2021/22

9. How many goals did Xabi Alonso score for Liverpool in European competitions?

    A. 48

    B. 38

    C. 28

    D. 18

10. Where was former Liverpool midfielder, Joe Allen, signed from?

    A. Stoke City

    B. Norwich City

    C. Southampton

    D. Swansea City

11. Which trophy did Charlie Adam win with Liverpool?

    A. FA Cup

    B. League Cup

    C. Premier League title

    D. UEFA Champions League

12. How many appearances in all competitions did Luis Alberto have in a Liverpool shirt?

    A. 15

    B. 14

    C. 13

    D. 12

13. Which of these midfielders won the PFA Player of the Year award in 1988?

    A. John Barnes

    B. John Aldridge

    C. John Bamber

    D. John Bovill

14. How many Premier League assists did Philippe Coutinho record for Liverpool?

    A. 40

    B. 35

    C. 30

    D. 25

15. Which of these Liverpool midfielders won the 2006 PFA Player of the Year?

    A. Xabi Alonso

    B. Paul Anderson

    C. Steven Gerrard

    D. Mohamed Sissoko

16. How many goals did Dietmar Hamann manage for Liverpool in all competitions?

    A. 14

    B. 13

    C. 12

    D. 11

17. Which country did Craig Johnston represent?

    A. Ireland

    B. Jamaica

    C. Portugal

    D. South Africa

18. How many Premier League goals did Gary McAllister score in a Liverpool shirt?

    A. 5

    B. 10

    C. 15

    D. 20

19. Against which of these clubs did Jamie Redknapp make his debut appearance for Liverpool?

    A. Aston Villa

    B. Auxerre

    C. Monaco

    D. Leeds United

20. How many FA Cup appearances did Xherdan Shaqiri manage for Liverpool in the 2020/21 season?

    A.   2

    B.   3

    C.   4

    D.   5

20 Trivia Answers

1. C – Emile Heskey

2. D – Middlesbrough

3. B – Jan Molby

4. A – Emlyn Hughes

5. A – Coventry City

6. D – Guinea

7. C – 2002

8. C – 2020/21

9. A – 48

10. D – Swansea City

11. B – League Cup

12. D – 12

13. A – John Barnes

14. B – 35

15. C – Steven Gerrard

16. D – 11

17. D – South Africa

18. A – 5

19. B – Auxerre

20. A - 2

10 Fun Facts

1. Versatile Scottish midfielder, John Wark, is the only Liverpool player who has scored a hattrick in three different competitions in the same season. In the 1984-85 season, he netted trebles against Lech Poznan in the European Cup at Anfield, York City in the FA Cup at Anfield, and away to West Bromwich Albion in the First Division.

2. Steve Heighway is the first Liverpool player to score in multiple FA Cup finals. He found the net in the 1971 FA Cup final defeat to Arsenal and scored again three years later to help the Reds to victory in Bill Shankly's final game as Liverpool manager.

3. Legendary English midfielder and club record appearance holder, Ian Callahan, was booked only once in 857 games for Liverpool. He received a yellow card from referee Pat Partridge in the 1978 League Cup final replay defeat against Nottingham Forest at Old Trafford.

4. During the 2014-15 season, Liverpool icon and legendary midfielder, Steven Gerrard, broke Billy Liddell's record that stood for nearly 55 years when he scored for a 16th consecutive season

5. Spanish midfielder, Antonio Nunez's only goal in the colours of Liverpool came in the 2005 League Cup final defeat to Chelsea. He still remains the only player whose only goal was scored in a final.

6. Former Chelsea and England midfielder, Joe Cole, joined Liverpool in 2010 and his first goal for the Red's turned out to be the fastest in European competition for the club. He found the back of the net after just 27 seconds against Steaua Bucharest at Anfield.

7. Steve McManaman was one of the greatest English midfielders of his time. His formidable partnership with Jaime Redknapp and Robbie Fowler earned the

trio the famous "Spice Boys" nickname. McManaman won one FA Cup and one League Cup in 9 years at Liverpool before moving to Real Madrid in 1999.

8. Scottish midfielder, Gary McAllister, is the oldest Liverpool goalscorer in the Merseyside derby. Aged 36 years and 112 days, he blasted home a 44-yard free kick in added time to help Liverpool edge a 3-2 thriller at Goodison Park in April 2001.

9. Liverpool midfielder, James Milner, has never lost a Premier League game in which he has scored in, including a run of 16 games between September 2009 and February 2015 in which his Aston Villa and Manchester City sides won every game he scored in.

10. Welsh midfielder, Ben Woodburn, is the youngest goalscorer in Liverpool history. His record-breaking goal came against Leeds United in a League Cup quarterfinal on 29 November 2016. He was aged 17 years and 45 days at the time.

FORWARDS

"Liverpool spoke to me and explained everything. They said I was really important. That made me very proud and at that point I focused my thoughts on Liverpool"

- Dirk Kuyt

20 Trivia Questions

1. In what year did Sadio Mane join Liverpool?

   A. 2014

   B. 2015

   C. 2016

   D. 2017

2. How many Premier League goals did Fernando Torres score in his first season at Liverpool?

   A. 20

   B. 24

   C. 26

   D. 28

3. Which of these clubs did Ian Rush play for between his two spells at Liverpool FC?

   A. Malmo

   B. Fenerbache

   C. Juventus

   D. Barcelona

4. Who did former Liverpool forward, Roger Hunt, play his last game against?

   A. Arsenal F.C

   B. Chelsea F.C

   C. Manchester United

   D. Tottenham Hotspur

5. How many league goals did Roger Hunt score in his last season with the club?

   A. 6

   B. 8

   C. 10

   D. 12

6. Which of these Liverpool forwards was affectionately known as 'super sub' in the 1970s and 1980s?

   A. David Fairclough

   B. Howard Gayle

   C. Colin Russell

   D. David Johnson

7. How many Champions League goals did Fernando Torres score for the club?

   A. 10

   B. 8

   C. 6

   D. 4

8. Which forward scored in the 1978 European Cup final against Club Brugge?

    A. Alan Hansen

    B. Kenny Daglish

    C. Ray Kennedy

    D. Emlyn Hughes

9. As of the end of 2020/21 season, how many goals did Firmino score in his most prolific season?

    A. 30

    B. 29

    C. 28

    D. 27

10. What is the full name of Jota?

    A. Diogo Jose Teixeria da Silva

    B. Diogo Jotinho da Silva Santos

    C. Diogo Carlos Silva

    D. Diogo Andre Silva

11. How many goals did Ian Rush score for Liverpool?

    A. 336

    B. 346

    C. 356

    D. 366

12. Which of these Liverpool strikers was nicknamed 'god' by many Liverpool fans?

    A. Ian Rush

    B. Roger Hunt

    C. Robbie Fowler

    D. Michael Owen

13. How many European Cups did Kenny Daglish win with the club?

    A. 2

    B. 3

    C. 4

    D. 5

14. Which club did David Fairclough play his debut match for Liverpool FC against?

    A. Hull City

    B. Southampton F.C

    C. Birmingham City

    D. Middlesbrough F.C

15. How many goals did Robbie Fowler score for Liverpool in European competitions?

    A. 14

    B. 16

    C. 18

    D. 20

16. Was the highest number of league goals Roger Hunt scored for Liverpool in a single season?

    A. 27

    B. 29

    C. 31

    D. 33

17. Where was former Liverpool forward, Dirk Kuyt, signed from?

    A. Utrecht

    B. PSV Eindhoven

    C. Ajax Amsterdam

    D. Feyenoord

18. Which club did Daniel Sturridge score his 50th Premier League goal for Liverpool against?

    A. Mansfield Town

    B. Everton F.C

    C. Southampton F.C

    D. Manchester City

19. Which of these former Liverpool forwards won the European Golden Boot?

    A. Michael Owen

    B. Fernando Torres

    C. Luis Suarez

    D. John Toshack

20. How many league cup trophies did Michael Owen win with Liverpool FC?

    A. 2

    B. 3

    C. 4

    D. 5

20 Trivia Answers

1. C – 2016

2. B – 24

3. C – Juventus

4. C – Manchester United

5. A – 6

6. A – David Fairclough

7. B – 8

8. B – Kenny Daglish

9. D – 27

10. A – Diogo Jose Teixeria da Silva

11. B – 346

12. C – Robbie Fowler

13. B – 3

14. D – Middlesbrough

15. A – 14

16. C – 31

17. D – Feyenoord

18. B – Everton

19. C – Luis Suarez

20. A – 2

10 Fun Facts

1. During his Liverpool career, Ian Rush scored in each of his seven New Year's Day appearances for the Reds. The first of such goals came in a hattrick against Notts County in 1983, and the last was scored against Ipswich Town in 1994.

2. Liverpool great, Jack Balmer, who spent his entire senior career with the Reds scored three successive hattrick in the league in 1946. He netted a treble against Portsmouth, a further quadruple away to Derby County and another three against Arsenal.

3. Legendary striker, Ian Rush, scored hattricks in six different competitions during his time at Anfield. The Welsh striker netted trebles in the First Division, FA Cup, League Cup, European Cup, UEFA Cup Winners Cup and Screen Sport Super Cup.

4. Forwards, John Aldridge (1989) and Djibril Cisse (2006), are the only Liverpool players to score first half goals in FA Cup finals. The other 19 goals scored by the Reds in FA Cup finals all came in the second half.

5. English forward Daniel Sturridge's solitary strike helped the Reds beat fierce rivals Manchester United 1-0 in a league game at Anfield in September 2013. In doing so, he became the 20th Liverpool player to score a goal for the club on their birthday.

6. Belgian striker, Divock Origi, is among the 15 players that have scored for Liverpool on every single day of the week. The list also includes forwards Mohamed Salah and Sadio Mane.

7. Egyptian forward, Mohamed Salah, is the 10th player to score 150 goals for Liverpool. He is also the second fastest to attain that milestone, doing so in 233 appearances. Roger Hunt amassed the same number in 226 games.

8. Following strikes against Norwich in February 2022, Liverpool forwards

Mohamed Salah and Sadio Mane have scored in the same Premier League match 30 times, the most for any pair of players from the same club.

9. Luiz Diaz is the first Colombian player to ever play for Liverpool. He joined the Reds from Portuguese club FC Porto for 37m pounds in January 2022. He was reportedly close to joining Tottenham Hotspur before the Reds swooped in and struck an agreement with Porto and his representatives.

10. Ian Rush, with 346 goals in 660 appearances, is the highest goalscorer in Liverpool history. The Wales striker also holds the record for most goals scored for Liverpool during a season, with 47 strikes in the 1983-84 season.

CAPTAINS

"Cut my veins open and I bleed Liverpool red. I love Liverpool with a burning passion"

- John Toshack

20 Trivia Questions

1. Who was the captain of Liverpool FC when they won the 2004/05 Champions League?

    A. Steven Gerrard

    B. Jordan Henderson

    C. Jamie Redknapp

    D. Sami Hyypia

2. Who replaced Steven Gerrard as the club's captain?

    A. Daniel Agger

    B. Jordan Henderson

    C. James Milner

    D. Martin Skrtel

3. Who did Steven Gerrard replace as the club's captain?

    A. Alan Hansen

    B. Robbie Fowler

    C. Jamie Redknapp

    D. Sami Hyypia

4. Who was Liverpool's first ever captain?

    A. George Allan

    B. Billy Dunlop

    C. Alex Raisebeck

    D. Andrew Hannah

5. Which of these club captains was famously called 'a colossus' by Bill Shankly?

    A. Tommy Smith

    B. Ron Yeats

    C. Emlyn Hughes

    D. Graeme Souness

6. Which of these players was the club's captain immediately after WWII?

    A. Willie Fagan

    B. Phil Taylor

    C. Tom Cooper

    D. Bill Jones

7. Who was the club's vice-captain during the 2015/16 season?

    A. Jordan Henderson

    B. James Milner

    C. Virgil Van Dijk

    D. Sadio Mane

8. Who was the club's captain during the 2000/01 season?

    A. Paul Ince

    B. John Barnes

    C. Jamie Redknapp

    D. Sami Hyypia

9. Who was Liverpool's vice-captain during the 2020/21 season?

    A. Virgil Van Dijk

    B. Jordan Henderson

    C. Lucas Leiva

    D. James Milner

10. Who was Liverpool's first ever vice-captain?

    A. Jimmy Ross

    B. Duncan McLean

    C. Matt McQueen

    D. John McCartney

11. During the 2002/03 season, who was the vice-captain of Liverpool?

    A. Sami Hyypia

    B. Jamie Redknapp

    C. Steven Gerrard

    D. Paul Ince

12. Which of these players was not a captain for the club?

    A. Kenny Daglish

    B. Emlyn Hughes

    C. Phil Thompson

    D. Graeme Souness

13. Which of these players was Liverpool's captain for only 3 games before WWII?

    A. Tom Cooper

    B. Willie Fagan

    C. Arthur Riley

    D. Matt Busby

14. As at the end of the 2020/21 season, who was Liverpool's longest serving captain?

    A. Jordan Henderson

    B. Steven Gerrard

    C. Jamie Redknapp

    D. Alan Hansen

15. Who was Liverpool's first ever 3rd captain?

    A. John McCartney

    B. Frank Becton

    C. George Allan

    D. Jimmy Ross

16. Who was Liverpool's 3rd captain during the 2012/13 season?

    A. Pepe Reina

    B. Luis Suarez

    C. Jordan Henderson

    D. Martin Skrtel

17. Who took over the club's captaincy from Ian Rush?

    A. Mark Wright

    B. Steve McManaman

    C. John Barnes

    D. Neil Ruddock

18. Which of these captains was affectionately known as 'jockey' by Liverpool fans?

    A. Alan Hansen

    B. Alex Raisbeck

    C. Don McKinlay

    D. Phil Thompson

19. Which of these Liverpool captains lifted the 2005 Champions League?

    A. Sami Hyypia

    B. Jordan Henderson

    C. Steven Gerrard

    D. Jamie Redknapp

20. Who took over the club captaincy from Willie Fagan?

    A.   Phil Taylor

    B.   Jack Balmer

    C.   Matt Busby

    D.   Laurie Hughes

20 Trivia Answers

1. A – Steven Gerrard

2. B – Jordan Henderson

3. D - Sami Hyypia

4. D – Andrew Hannah

5. B – Ron Yeats

6. A – Willie Fagan

7. B – James Milner

8. C – Jamie Redknapp

9. D – James Milner

10. B – Duncan McLean

11. C – Steven Gerrard

12. A – Kenny Daglish

13. D – Matt Busby

14. B – Steven Gerrard

15. D – Jimmy Ross

16. B – Luis Suarez

17. C – John Barnes

18. A – Alan Hansen

19. C – Steven Gerrard

20. B – Jack Balmer

10 Fun Facts

1. Jordan Henderson joined Liverpool from Sunderland in 2011 and played a bit part as the Reds reached the finals of the FA Cup and the League Cup in his first season. Five years later, he was made captain following the departure of fellow midfielder and club icon Steven Gerrard. He led the club to its first league title in 30 years during the 2019-20 season.

2. Bill Shankly introduced Emlyn Hughes as a future England captain following his move to Liverpool from Blackpool in 1967. Hughes made 665 appearances for the Reds, leading them to 4 league titles and 1 FA Cup in the 1970s. He became the first Liverpool captain to lift the European Cup in 1977.

3. Phil Thompson was an integral figure of the great Liverpool sides of the 1970s and 1980s. Across his 13-year stay and over 300 appearances, the English defender helped the Reds to seven league titles and led the club to European Cup final success against Real Madrid in 1981 as captain.

4. Scottish centreback, Alex Raisbeck, was arguably the first star player in Liverpool history following his move to Anfield in 1898 from Hibernian for a surprisingly low sum of 350 pounds. During his 11-year stay, he captained the Reds to a maiden First Division title in 1900-01. When the club suffered its first relegation in 1903-04, he led them straight back up by winning the Second Division and followed that up with another First Division title in 1905-06.

5. Legendary Liverpool defender, Ron Yeats, was made club captain just 6 months on from his move to the Reds from Dundee United. He immediately led the club back to the old First Division in his first season at the club. Silverware soon followed with a first FA Cup win in 1965 sandwiched between two championship titles.

6. Steven Gerrard is arguably the most symbolic figure in Liverpool history and one of the best players of his generation. His wide array of skills and inspirational leadership style endeared him to teammates, managers and fans all over the world. The high point of his captaincy was the famous "Miracle of Istanbul" when he led the charge from 3-0 down at halftime to level the scores and win the UEFA Champions League on penalties in 2005.

7. Club record goalscorer Ian Rush only became captain towards the end of his second spell at Liverpool, leading the club to a League Cup win in 1995.

8. Sami Hyppia assumed the role of captain due to circumstances which forced then captain Jaime Redknapp and vice-captain Robbie Fowler to miss large chunks of the 200-01 season. He led the club to pieces of silverware in 2001 and the League Cup in 2003 before being replaced with Steven Gerrard in the 2003-04 season.

9. Don McKinlay broke into the Liverpool first team in 1910 and went on to serve the club meritoriously for 18 years. He made 434 appearances and scored 34 goals within this period. He was made captain in 1921 amidst a 15-year title drought at Liverpool and he made it his personal mission to bring championship success back to Anfield. He came good on his promise as the Reds clinched the First Division in his first season as captain. He also led the club to a successful defense of the league title the following season, becoming the first Liverpool captain to win the title in successive seasons.

10. One of the finest and most complete midfielders of his generation, Graeme Souness, joined Liverpool in January 1978 and became captain in 1981. He was the first captain to lift the First Division in 3 consecutive seasons, and also the first captain to lead his side to league and cup doubles in 3 successive seasons. These feats were achieved between the 1981-82 and 1983-84 seasons.

CHAPTER

9

TITLES

"Liverpool Football Club exists to win trophies"

- Bill Shankly

20 Trivia Questions

1. When did Liverpool win their first European trophy?

    A. 1970

    B. 1971

    C. 1972

    D. 1973

2. In what year did Liverpool win their 18th English League title?

    A. 1985

    B. 1990

    C. 1995

    D. 2002

3. In which year did Liverpool win their first FA Cup?

    A. 1960

    B. 1963

    C. 1965

    D. 1968

4. Which club did Liverpool defeat to win the 1977 European Cup?

    A.   Manchester United

    B.   Sporting CP

    C.   Borussia Moenchengladbach

    D.   AS Roma

5. Which club did Liverpool FC beat to win the 2005 UEFA Champions League?

    A.   Inter Milan

    B.   AC Milan

    C.   Bayern Munich

    D.   Real Madrid

6. In what season did Liverpool win their first ever Division 2 title?

    A.   1892/93

    B.   1893/94

    C.   1894/95

    D.   1895/96

7. In what season did Liverpool win their second Division 2 title?

    A.   1895/96

    B.   1896/97

    C.   1897/98

    D.   1898/99

8. Since the establishment of the Premier League in 1992, how many Premier League title(s) has Liverpool won?

    A. 1

    B. 3

    C. 5

    D. 7

9. How many times did Liverpool win the Football League Division 2 title?

    A. 2

    B. 4

    C. 6

    D. 8

10. In what year did Liverpool FC win their first FIFA Club World Cup?

    A. 2017

    B. 2015

    C. 2019

    D. 2021

11. Which club did Liverpool FC defeat to win the 1984 European Cup?

    A. Bayern Munich

    B. Roma

    C. Juventus

    D. Real Madrid

12. Which club did Liverpool FC defeat to win the 2001 UEFA Cup?

    A. Shakhtar Donetsk

    B. PSV Eindhoven

    C. Bayer Leverkusen

    D. Alaves

13. As at the end of the 2021/22 season, how many European Cups has the club won?

    A. 5

    B. 6

    C. 7

    D. 8

14. Which club did Liverpool FC defeat to win the 2019 FIFA Club World Cup?

    A. Esperance de Tunis

    B. Al-Hilal

    C. Monterrey

    D. Flamengo

15. As of the end of the 2021/22 season, how many English League titles has Liverpool won?

    A. 17

    B. 18

    C. 19

    D. 20

16. How many points did Liverpool accrue to win the 2019/20 Premier League title?

    A.   100

    B.   99

    C.   98

    D.   97

17. Which club did Liverpool defeat to win the League Cup in 2012?

    A.   Cardiff City

    B.   Birmingham City

    C.   Chelsea

    D.   Manchester City

18. How many times have Liverpool won the European Super Cup?

    A.   7

    B.   6

    C.   5

    D.   4

19. When was the last time Liverpool won the UEFA Europa League?

    A.   2003

    B.   2002

    C.   2001

    D.   2000

20. Before Liverpool won the 2019/20 Premier League title, when was the last time they had won the title?

    A.   1988/89

    B.   1989/90

    C.   1990/91

    D.   1991/92

20 Trivia Answers

1. D – 1973

2. B – 1990

3. C – 1965

4. D – Borussia Monchengladbach

5. B – AC Milan

6. B – 1893/94

7. A – 1895/96

8. A – 1

9. B – 4

10. C – 2019

11. B – Roma

12. D – Alaves

13. B – 6

14. D – Flamengo

15. C – 19

16. B – 99

17. A – Cardiff City

18. D – 4

19. C – 2001

20. B – 1989/90

10 Fun Facts

1. In their first ever season, Liverpool won the Lancashire league. They also won the Football League Second Division at their first attempt, achieving promotion to the First Division.

2. Liverpool won the First division title for the first time in 1901. They have since gone on to add 18 more top flight titles, just one behind Manchester United who have won it a record 20 times.

3. Liverpool is the most successful club in the history of the English Football League Cup, with a total of eight triumphs. Their last success came in 2012 against Cardiff City on penalties.

4. Liverpool are the most successful English team in Europe, winning the European Cup/UEFA Champions League six times, the UEFA Cup three times and the UEFA Super Cup four times.

5. Liverpool have won 3 titles in a single season on two separate occasions. They won the First Division title, the European Cup and the League Cup in 1983-84 and also won the UEFA Cup, the FA Cup and the League Cup in 2000-01.

6. Liverpool's triumph in the 2005 UEFA Champions League made them one of only four teams to have won the competition from the third qualification round.

7. Liverpool have only ever won the League and FA Cup double once, doing so in 1985-86 during the first season of Sir Kenneth Dalglish as player-manager. However, they have won the League and Football League Cup double on two occasions. They have also achieved a cup double three times.

8. Liverpool became only the second English side to win the FIFA Club World Cup when they beat Brazilian side Flamengo 1-0 in the final in December 2019.

Brazilian striker, Roberto Firmino, scored the winner in extra time.

9. Liverpool are the first British club to have won successive European Cups. The Reds captured continental football's greatest prize for the first time in 1977 and repeated the feat a year later.

10. Liverpool's haul of 43 major honours is the most by an English club. Rivals Manchester United have the next best record, with 42 major titles won.

MEMORABLE GAMES

"The last half an hour against Dortmund [in the Europa League at Anfield] is the best I've ever had. I felt nobody could stop us. I wasn't sure we would score a goal but it was crazy"

- *Jurgen Klopp*

20 Trivia Questions

1. Who were the unlucky recipients of Liverpool's biggest European scoreline?

   A. Stromsgodset Drammen

   B. Ferencvaros

   C. Real Zaragoza

   D. Ludogorets Razgrad

2. What was the scoreline of Liverpool's largest away Premier League win?

   A. 8:0

   B. 9:0

   C. 7:0

   D. 6:0

3. Who were the opponents when Liverpool recorded their biggest league victory?

   A. Middlesbrough

   B. Plymouth

   C. Rotherham Town

   D. Huddersfield Town

4. Which club did Liverpool defeat to win their first ever FIFA Club World Cup?

    A. Monterrey

    B. Flamengo

    C. Al-Hilal

    D. Esperance de Tunis

5. Which club handed Liverpool their heaviest FA Cup defeat?

    A. Aston Villa

    B. Manchester United

    C. Bolton Wanderers

    D. Manchester City

6. On the first day of June 2019, Liverpool defeated Tottenham Hotspur to win the Champions League final. what was the scoreline?

    A. 2:0

    B. 2:1

    C. 1:0

    D. 3:1

7. Who was Liverpool's first ever Football League match opponent?

    A. Rotherham Town

    B. Ipswich

    C. Luton Town

    D. Middlesbrough Ironopolis

8. Against which club did Liverpool's record Premier League away win come?

    A. Aston Villa

    B. Birmingham

    C. Crystal Palace

    D. Derby County

9. Against which club did Liverpool record their biggest FA Cup win?

    A. Crystal Palace

    B. Newton

    C. Reading

    D. Norwich City

10. Who were the opponents for Liverpool's record league home attendance?

    A. Manchester United

    B. Manchester City

    C. Arsenal F.C

    D. Chelsea F.C

11. Who were the opponents for the record attendance (for a non-competitive match) in Liverpool's history?

    A. Adelaide FC

    B. Melbourne Victory

    C. Barcelona FC

    D. Manchester United

12. Steven Gerrard's last game at Anfield ended in a 3:1 defeat for Liverpool. Who were the opponents?

    A. Stoke City

    B. Crystal Palace

    C. West Brom

    D. Burnley

13. Liverpool won the Merseyside derby in March 2012 by defeating Everton by three goals. Who scored all three goals?

    A. Fernando Torres

    B. Dirk Kuyt

    C. Daniel Sturridge

    D. Steven Gerrard

14. Which of these players scored a hattrick when Liverpool thrashed Manchester United 4:0 in September 1990?

    A. Peter Beardsley

    B. Kenny Dalglish

    C. Ian Rush

    D. John Barnes

15. Robbie Fowler scored one of the fastest Premier League hattricks in August 1994. Who were the opponents?

    A. Arsenal F.C

    B. Brighton and Hove Albion

    C. Chelsea F.C

    D. Tottenham Hotspur F.C

16. The widely-adjudged Premier League's Match of the Decade in the 90s was between Liverpool and which club?

    A. Arsenal F.C

    B. Sunderland F.C

    C. Manchester United

    D. Newcastle F.C

17. Who were the opponents when Michael Owen made his debut for Liverpool?

    A. Portsmouth F.C

    B. MK Dons

    C. Wimbledon F.C

    D. Reading F.C

18. Who scored the extra time goal that made Liverpool winners of the 2001 European Cup?

    A. Gary McAllister

    B. Delfi Geli

    C. Steven Gerrard

    D. Sami Hyypia

19. During the 2004/05 UEFA Champions League group stage, who scored the winning goal that sent the club into the knockout stages?

    A. Steven Gerrard

    B. Michael Owen

    C. Florent Pongolle

    D. Luis Garcia

20. In 1997, 17-year-old Michael Owen scored his first hattrick for Liverpool in a League Cup tie. Who were the opponents?

    A.   Sheffield Wednesday

    B.   Sheffield United

    C.   Grimsby

    D.   Newcastle

20 Trivia Answers

1. A – Stromsgodset Drammen

2. C – 7:0

3. C – Rotherham Town

4. B – Flamengo

5. C – Bolton Wanderers

6. A – 2:0

7. D – Middlesbrough Ironopolis

8. C – Crystal Palace

9. B – Newton

10. D – Chelsea

11. D – Manchester United

12. B – Crystal Palace

13. D – Steven Gerrard

14. A – Peter Beardsley

15. A – Arsenal

16. D – Newcastle

17. C – Wimbledon

18. B – Delfi Geli

19. A – Steven Gerrard

20. C – Grimsby

10 Fun Facts

1. The 2018/19 UEFA Champions League final on June 1, 2019 was the first time Liverpool have played a competitive match in the month of June. The Reds ran out 2-0 victors courtesy of goals from Mohamed Salah and Divock Origi.

2. Ian Rush scored four goals and Mark Lawrenson netted the other as Liverpool routed local rivals Everton 5-0 in a league game at Goodison Park. The hosts had Glenn Keely sent off on 37 minutes for cynically holding Kenny Dalglish as the talented Liverpool great appeared to have a clear run at Everton's goal.

3. Liverpool scored 3 goals in 6 second half minutes to draw level with AC Milan in the 2005 UEFA Champions League final. The Italian side had raced into a 3-goal halftime lead courtesy of Paolo Maldini and Hernan Crespo. The Reds triumphed 3-2 on penalties in what is arguably the most memorable final in Liverpool history.

4. Liverpool's fourth European Cup success came at the scene of their first – the eternal city of Rome. The Reds defeated home side AS Roma 4-2 on penalties following a 1-1 draw to claim their fourth European Cup in just 8 seasons.

5. Any win at the backyard of a fierce rival is exciting and even more memorable if it's by five goals. Liverpool trounced Manchester United 5-0 in a Premier League game at Old Trafford on October 24 2021. Mohamed Salah netted a hattrick to complement the Reds' first two goals from Naby Keita and Diogo Jota.

6. In what became an instant Premier League classic and one of the best league games in the current era, Liverpool edged eventual champions Manchester City 4-3 at Anfield to put a dent in what had until then been a near-perfect march by the visitors towards the Premier League title. Alex Oxlade-Chamberlain, Roberto Firmino, Mohamed Salah and Sadio Mane were all on the scoresheet for the Reds.

7. Despite coming short at the final hurdle, Liverpool's run to the 2016 Europa League final will not easily be forgotten especially among the Reds' faithful. One match that stood out in particular is the quarterfinal second leg at home to Borussia Dortmund. The tie was finely poised following a 1-1 draw at Germany but the Reds found themselves 2 goals down after ten minutes and 1-3 down near the hour mark, needing 3 goals to progress. Liverpool rallied to level the scores before Dejan Lovren powered home an injury time winner to send Anfield into delirium.

8. The final against AC Milan attracts most of the spotlight in most reviews of Liverpool's run to UEFA Champions League glory in 2005. In hindsight, the seeds of that triumph were most likely sown during the last group game at home to Olympiacos. The Reds went into that game knowing they needed to win by 2 goals to progress from the first round. Their task was made even harder when Brazil legend Rivaldo rifled home a 26th minute freekick after he was fouled on the edge of the box. An inspired second half saw Liverpool equalize and go in front largely thanks to goals from substitutes Sinama Pongolle and Neil Mellor, before Steven Gerrard struck home a sweet volley that almost tore the roof off Anfield.

9. In one of the more recent great European nights at Anfield, Liverpool overcame a 3-0 first leg deficit to knock out Spanish heavyweights Barcelona in the semifinal of the 2018-19 UEFA Champions League. The Reds' task was made even more complicated due to the absences of key forwards Roberto Firmino and Mohamed Salah for the second leg. However, the Reds' triumphed 4-0 courtesy of a pair of braces from Divock Origi and Giorgino Wijnaldum.

10. Liverpool thrashed Tottenham Hotspur 5-0 in one of the matches that laid down a marker for the Reds' title tilt during the 2013-14 Premier League season. The Reds' trio of Luis Suarez, Raheem Sterling and Jordan Henderson were particularly unplayable, in one of the best Reds display away from home in the Premier League.

BIGGEST TRANSFERS
(HIDDEN GEMS AND MASSIVE DEALS)

"It is important for the club to find a balance in a world driven by economic and political needs. This club usually does that"

- Gerard Houllier

20 Trivia Questions

1. Who is Liverpool's most expensive signing?

    A. Fabinho

    B. Naby Keita

    C. Virgil van Dijk

    D. Mohammed Salah

2. Which of these players is the club's 3rd most expensive sale?

    A. Raheem Sterling

    B. Fernando Torres

    C. Christian Benteke

    D. Luiz Suarez

3. How much did Liverpool receive from the transfer of Phillipe Coutinho to Barcelona?

    A. £135m

    B. £100m

    C. £85m

    D. £75m

4. Which club was Mohammed Salah signed from?

    A. Basel

    B. Chelsea

    C. Roma

    D. Fiorentina

5. Which striker did Liverpool FC sign for a club record fee of £111,000 in 1970?

    A. Alun Evans

    B. John Toshack

    C. Bobby Graham

    D. Jack Whitman

6. Which player attracted the second highest transfer sale fee?

    A. Fernando Torres

    B. Emre Can

    C. Raheem Sterling

    D. Luis Suarez

7. Which of these players did Liverpool sign for £35 million from Arsenal?

    A. Theo Walcott

    B. Adam Lallana

    C. Alex Oxlade Chamberlain

    D. Robbie Keane

8. Who is currently the most expensive Liverpool midfield signing?

    A. Thiago Alcantara

    B. Adam Lallana

    C. Naby Keita

    D. Javier Mascherano

9. Which of these former Liverpool players was signed for less than £20 million?

    A. Luis Suarez

    B. Stewart Downing

    C. Alberto Aquilani

    D. Mario Balotelli

10. Which Liverpool forward holds the record for the highest transfer fee paid?

    A. Christian Benteke

    B. Luis Diaz

    C. Mohamed Salah

    D. Sadio Mane

11. Who is the club's most expensive summer signing?

    A. Mohammed Salah

    B. Alisson Becker

    C. Virgil Van Dijk

    D. Christian Benteke

12. As at the end of the 2001/02 season, who was Liverpool's most expensive sale?

    A. El-Hadji Diouf

    B. Michael Owen

    C. Robbie Fowler

    D. Emile Heskey

13. Who is the club's second most expensive defender?

    A. Dejan Lovren

    B. Alberto Moreno

    C. Glen Johnson

    D. Ibrahima Konate

14. Who was Liverpool's most expensive signing during the 2014/15 summer transfer window?

    A. Mario Balotelli

    B. Adam Lallana

    C. Dejan Lovren

    D. Emre Can

15. During the 2004/05 summer transfer window, who was the club's most expensive signing?

    A. Djibril Cisse

    B. Luis Garcia

    C. Antonio Nunez

    D. El-Hadj Diouf

16. Who is the most expensive Liverpool midfielder signed during the winter transfer window?

    A. Daniel Sjolund

    B. Javier Mascherano

    C. Igor Biscan

    D. Jamie Redknapp

17. Ibrahima Konate completed a £36 million transfer move to Liverpool. Which club sanctioned the sale?

    A. Atletico Madrid

    B. R.B Leipzig

    C. Werder Bremen

    D. Napoli

18. Which of these players arrived the club on loan during the 2020/21 season?

    A. Ozan Kabak

    B. Javier Manquillo

    C. Emiliano Insua

    D. Daniele Padelli

19. Which of these players was Liverpool's most expensive sale in the 2021/22 summer transfer window?

    A. Georginio Wijnaldum

    B. Xherdan Shaqiri

    C. Taiwo Awoniyi

    D. Harry Wilson

20. Which of these players did Liverpool sign on a free transfer?

 A. Nathaniel Clyne

 B. Robbie Keane

 C. Joel Matip

 D. Xherdan Shaqiri

20 Trivia Answers

1. C – Virgil Van Dijk

2. B – Fernando Torres

3. A - £135m

4. C – Roma

5. B - John Toshack

6. D - Luis Suarez

7. C – Alex Oxlade Chamberlain

8. C – Naby Keita

9. D – Mario Balotelli

10. B – Christian Benteke

11. B – Alisson Becker

12. C – Robbie Fowler

13. D – Ibrahima Konate

14. B – Adam Lallana

15. A - Djibril Cisse

16. C – Igor Biscan

17. B – Leipzig

18. A – Ozan Kabak

19. D – Harry Wilson

20. C – Joel Matip

10 Fun Facts

1. English centre forward, Albert Stubbins, was recruited in 1946 for a record fee of 12,500 pounds from Newcastle United. He scored 83 goals in 187 games for the Reds and helped the club win the First Division in 1947.

2. Finnish centreback, Sami Hyppia, joined Liverpool from Dutch Eredivisie side Willem II in 1999 for just 2.6m pounds. He would go on to form a formidable partnership with Jamie Carragher, leading the club to a treble of cup successes in 2001. He also helped the club clinch a fifth European crown in 2005 scoring a remarkable volley in the UEFA Champions League quarter final win against Juventus.at Anfield. He left the club in 2009 following a decade of meritorious service.

3. Dutch defender, Virgil van Dijk, is the most expensive recruit in Liverpool history. The imposing centreback joined the Reds from fellow Premier League side Southampton for 75m pounds in January 2018. He has since helped the club to UEFA Champions League and Premier League title successes in his first two full seasons.

4. Brazilian midfielder Phillipe Coutinho is the most expensive player ever sold by Liverpool. He left the club for Spanish giants, Barcelona, in a deal worth about 145m pounds in January 2018 after spending 5 years at Anfield.

5. Upon taking over the manager's job at Anfield, Rafael Benitez acquired the services of Xabi Alonso from Real Sociedad for a princely sum of 11m pounds. The Spaniard went on to form a formidable partnership with Steven Gerrard in the Reds' midfield, helping the club to UEFA Champions League and FA Cup triumphs in his first two seasons at the club. The club reached another Champions League final in 2007, before he left in 2009.

6. Brazilian goalkeeper, Alisson Becker, joined Liverpool for 67m pounds in the summer of 2018, a record fee for a goalkeeper at the time. The club were convinced he was the solution to their goalkeeper troubles as he had helped AS Roma reach the last 4 in the previous season's Champions League. He kept 27 clean sheets in all competitions in his first season at the club and helped win the UEFA Champions League and a first Premier League title.

7. Liverpool fought off strong competition from rivals Manchester United to seal a 20m pounds move for Fernando Torres from Atletico Madrid. The Spaniard became a fan favourite immediately with a composed finish on his Anfield debut against Chelsea. He scored 81 goals in 142 appearances before moving to Chelsea in January 2011.

8. Luis Suarez joined Liverpool for 23m pounds on the final day of the January transfer window in 2011, moments before the sale of Fernando Torres was finalized. The Uruguayan became an instant hit, scoring a lot of marvelous and important goals for the Reds. His haul of 31 Premier League goals in 2013/14 was at the time, a joint record high for a 38-game Premier League season.

9. It took many by surprise when Liverpool parted with 34m pounds to secure the services of Egyptian Forward Mohamed Salah from AS Roma in 2017, considering the fact that he did not make much of an impact during his 2 years stay at Chelsea between 2013 and 2015. He immediately confounded his doubters though, scoring a remarkable 44 goals in all competitions in his first season and helping Liverpool to a first Champions League final in 11 years.

10. Liverpool signed Scottish defender, Andrew Robertson, from recently relegated Hull City in 2017 for just 8m pounds. The Scot has made the Reds left back position his own and alongside Trent Alexander-Arnold formed one of the most fearsome fullback partnerships in European club football.

RECORD BREAKERS

"When I die, don't bring me to the hospital. Bring me to Anfield. I was born there and I will die there."

- Steven Gerrard

20 Trivia Questions

1. Which of these players holds the record for the most consecutive appearances for the club?

    A. Emlyn Hughes

    B. Alan Hansen

    C. Tommy Smith

    D. Phil Neal

2. Which player holds the record for most league goals for the club?

    A. Ian Rush

    B. Roger Hunt

    C. Gordon Hodgson

    D. Steven Gerrard

3. Who is the club's all-time leading goal scorer?

    A. Ian Rush

    B. Roger Hunt

    C. Gordon Hodgson

    D. Steven Gerrard

4. Which of these players has the most appearances for the club?

    A. Jamie Carragher

    B. Ray Clemence

    C. Steven Gerrard

    D. Ian Callaghan

5. Who was the club's first ever substitute?

    A. Geoff Strong

    B. Thomas Lowry

    C. Tommy Smith

    D. Gordon Wallace

6. Which Liverpool player holds the record for the most goals scored in a debut season?

    A. Fernando Torres

    B. Sadio Mane

    C. Mohammed Salah

    D. Roberto Firmino

7. Who is Liverpool FC's record goalscorer in Europe?

    A. Ian Rush

    B. Steven Gerrard

    C. Roger Hunt

    D. Ian Callaghan

8. Who is the oldest first-team player to feature for Liverpool FC?

    A. Gary McAllister

    B. Sami Hyypia

    C. Bruce Grobbelaar

    D. Ned Doig

9. Who holds the record for the fastest Premier League hattrick for Liverpool FC?

    A. Gordon Hodgson

    B. Michael Owen

    C. Robbie Fowler

    D. Luiz Suarez

10. Which of these players has the most appearances for the club in Europe?

    A. Jamie Carragher

    B. Jerome Sinclair

    C. Elisha Scott

    D. Phil Neal

11. Who was the club's youngest first-team player?

    A. Michael Owen

    B. Alan A'Court

    C. Jerome Sinclair

    D. Jordan Rossiter

12. Who is the youngest goalscorer in the club's history?

    A.   Ben Woodburn

    B.   Raheem Sterling

    C.   Jimmy Melia

    D.   Michael Owen

13. Which of these players holds the record for most red cards as a Liverpool player?

    A.   Jamie Carragher

    B.   Alan Kennedy

    C.   Steven Gerrard

    D.   John Arne Riise

14. Who was the first player to score a goal for Liverpool FC?

    A.   Malcolm McVean

    B.   John Hunter

    C.   Peter Kyle

    D.   Abraham Foxall

15. Which of these players has the most hat-tricks for the Club?

    A.   Robbie Fowler

    B.   Gordon Hodgson

    C.   Ian Rush

    D.   Roger Hunt

16. Who scored Liverpool's fastest ever Premier League goal?

    A. Steven Gerrard

    B. Maxi Rodriguez

    C. Stan Collymore

    D. Naby Keita

17. Which Liverpool player scored the first goal to be shown on BBC's *Match of the Day*?

    A. Gordon Wallace

    B. Ian Callaghan

    C. Roger Hunt

    D. Ian St John

18. Which of these players scored the club's first Premier League goal?

    A. Paul Stewart

    B. Jamie Redknapp

    C. Jan Molby

    D. Mark Walters

19. Which of these Liverpool players made the 2018/19 PFA Team of the Year?

    A. Mohamed Salah

    B. Trent Alexander-Arnold

    C. Alisson Becker

    D. Jordan Henderson

20. Who is the oldest player to score a goal for Liverpool FC?

    A. David Fairclough

    B. Harry Chambers

    C. Billy Liddell

    D. Roger Hunt

20 Trivia Answers

1. D – Phil Neal

2. B – Roger Hunt

3. A – Ian Rush

4. D – Ian Callaghan

5. A – Geoff Strong

6. C – Mohammed Salah

7. B – Steven Gerrard

8. D – Ned Doig

9. C – Robbie Fowler

10. A – Jamie Carragher

11. C – Jerome Sinclair

12. A – Ben Woodburn

13. C – Steven Gerrard

14. A – Malcolm McVean

15. B – Gordon Hodgson

16. D – Naby Keita

17. C – Roger Hunt

18. D – Mark Walters

19. B – Trent Alexander-Arnold

20. C – Billy Liddell

10 Fun Facts

1. Liverpool's first ever England captain, Eph Longworth (370), fullback Rob Jones (243) and centre back Stephane Henchoz (205) all made over 200 appearances for the Reds without finding the back of the net.

2. Guinean midfielder, Naby Keita, scored Liverpool's quickest Premier League goal in a demolition of Huddersfield Town in April 2019 at Anfield. The Reds' 2 other African players Mohamed Salah and Sadio Mane scored a brace each to complete a 5-0 rout.

3. Liverpool have contested the final of a major trophy in the three different countries of mainland Britain. Those finals came in the cities of London, Glasgow, and Cardiff

4. Robbie Fowler scored Liverpool's quickest Premier League hattrick in just 4 minutes and 33 seconds against Arsenal in 1994. It stood as a Premier League record for more than 2 decades, before current Liverpool forward Sadio Mane, then at Southampton, scored 3 in 2 minutes and 56 seconds against Aston Villa in May 2015.

5. Mohamed Salah holds the record for most goals scored over the course of a 38-game Premier League season. His 32 strikes in 2017/18 broke the record set by Cristiano Ronaldo and Luis Suarez who scored 31 goals each in 2007/08 and 2013/14 seasons respectively.

6. Elisha Scott is the longest serving player in the club's history. The Northern Irish goalkeeper spent almost 22 years at the club making over 400 appearances and picking up a couple of First Division titles along the way.

7. Jerome Sinclair is the youngest player to ever feature for Liverpool, making his debut at the tender age of 16 years and 6 days against his boyhood club West Bromwich Albion in a League Cup win for the Reds in September 2012.

8. Liverpool legend, Billy Liddell, is the oldest goalscorer in the club's history. At 38 years and 55 days, he scored in a 5-1 Liverpool win against Stoke City in March 1960. His influence was so huge the club was nicknamed "Liddellpool" during his playing days.

9. Phil Neal was the first signing of the Paisley era and became the most decorated player in Liverpool history. He won 8 league titles, 4 European Cups, 4 League Cups, 5 Charity Shields, 1 UEFA Cup and 1 UEFA Super Cup. He also made the most consecutive appearances for the club with 417. He played every single minute of all league and cup games for 9 successive seasons from 1974/75 to 1982/83

10. Club icon, Steven Gerrard, received 6 red cards, the most of any player in the club's history. His last red card came just 38 seconds after coming on as a substitute against Manchester United in a Premier League game at Anfield in 2015.

A Short Message from The House of Ballers team

Hello fellow sports fanatic, we hope you enjoyed The Best Liverpool FC Trivia Book Ever.

We'd like to thank you for purchasing and reading it to the end.

We create these books to allow people to, not just expand their knowledge around their favorite clubs and players, but also to keep the passion we all have for the game lit and alive.

Life can come with many challenges and setbacks. But something that never leaves our side is our love for the game.

If you enjoyed reading this book, we'd like to kindly ask for your feedback and thoughts in the review section on Amazon.com.

This will help us continue to make the highest quality books and content for fans all across the world.

>> Scan the QR Code below with your smartphone to leave a short review <<

Ball out,

The House of Ballers Team

Printed in Great Britain
by Amazon

14855363R00078